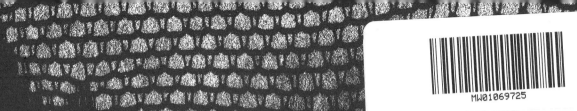

MW01069725

EL LARGO TREN OSCURO

by Samuel Hiti

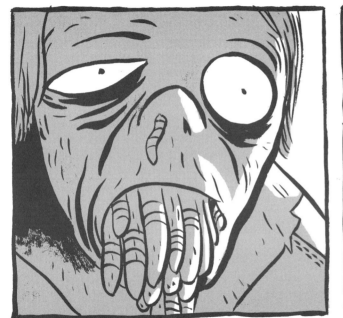

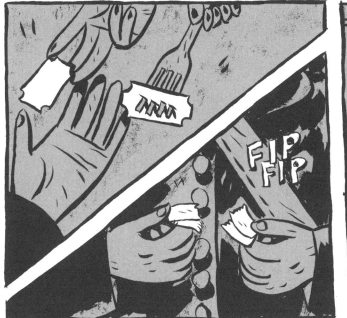

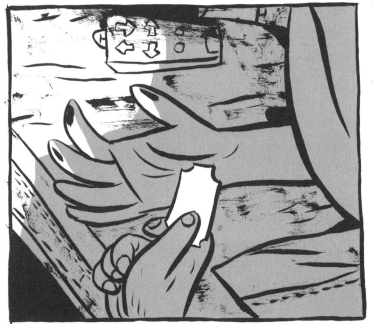

¡LOS BOLETOS!

...SU BoleTo...

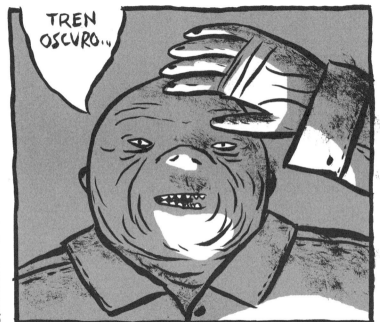

TUNK
TUNK

keeek

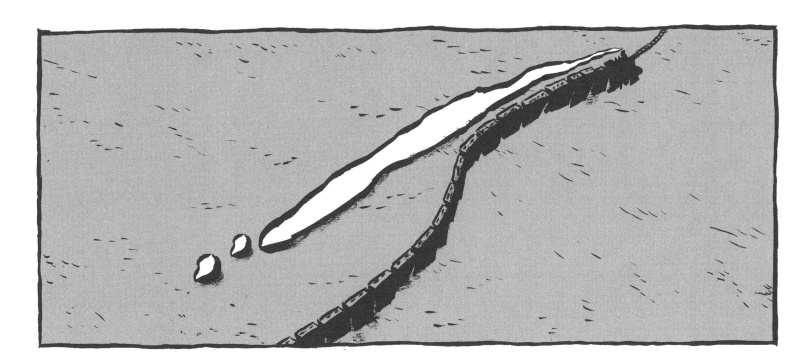

EL LARGO TREN OSCURO; COPY RIGHT ©2005 SAMUEL HITI published by La Luz Comics. ALL Rights Reserved.

ALL characters Featured in this Book, the distinctive likeness there-of, and all related indicia are Trademarks of Samuel Hiti. No portion of this Book may be used in any way, without the permission of samuel, exept for Review purpose.

Printed, bound, and made in Minnesota
First Edition: May 2005
www.samhiti.com
ISBN: 0-9755193-1-X
10 9 8 7 6 5 4 3 2 1